SCIENCE STARTERS

SUPER MATERIALS

Wendy Madgwick

RSVP
RAINTREE
STECK-VAUGHN
P U B L I S H E R S
A Steck-Vaughn Company

Austin, Texas

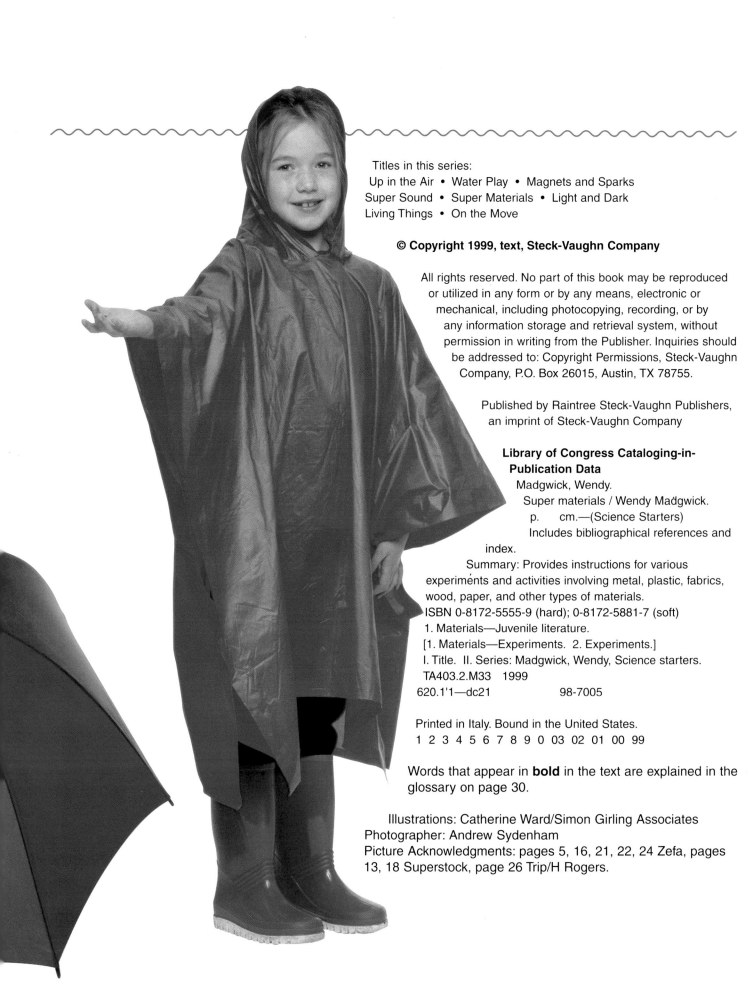

Titles in this series:
Up in the Air • Water Play • Magnets and Sparks
Super Sound • Super Materials • Light and Dark
Living Things • On the Move

Published by Raintree Steck-Vaughn Publishers, an imprint of Steck-Vaughn Company

Library of Congress Cataloging-in-Publication Data
Madgwick, Wendy.
    Super materials / Wendy Madgwick.
        p.   cm.—(Science Starters)
        Includes bibliographical references and index.
    Summary: Provides instructions for various experiments and activities involving metal, plastic, fabrics, wood, paper, and other types of materials.
    ISBN 0-8172-5555-9 (hard); 0-8172-5881-7 (soft)
    1. Materials—Juvenile literature.
    [1. Materials—Experiments. 2. Experiments.]
    I. Title. II. Series: Madgwick, Wendy, Science starters.
    TA403.2.M33   1999
    620.1'1—dc21   98-7005

Printed in Italy. Bound in the United States.
1 2 3 4 5 6 7 8 9 0 03 02 01 00 99

Words that appear in **bold** in the text are explained in the glossary on page 30.

Illustrations: Catherine Ward/Simon Girling Associates
Photographer: Andrew Sydenham
Picture Acknowledgments: pages 5, 16, 21, 22, 24 Zefa, pages 13, 18 Superstock, page 26 Trip/H Rogers.

Contents

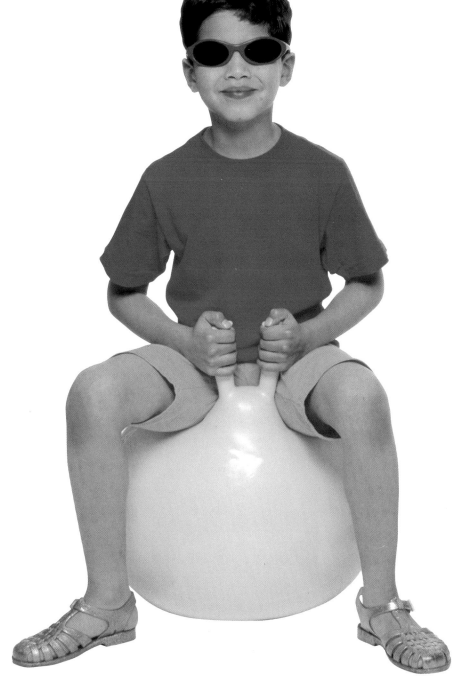

Looking at Materials

Materials such as metal, plastic, fabrics, wood, paper, and glass are all around you. With this book you can have lots of fun finding out about materials. Here are some simple rules you should follow before doing an activity:

- Tell an adult what you are doing, and ask if you can do the activity.
- Always read through the activity before you start.
- Collect all the materials you will need. They are listed on page 28.
- Make sure you have enough space to set up your activity.
- Follow each step carefully. Ask an adult to help if you need to.
- Watch what happens carefully and keep a notebook. Draw pictures or write down what you did and what happened.
- Never put any of the things you test in your mouth (except for the chocolate rabbits you can make on page 25!)
- Always clear up when you have finished. Wash your hands.

► When rock becomes very hot, it **melts**. You can see streams of hot liquid rock pouring out of this erupting volcano.

What's What?

We use lots of different materials to make things. Some materials come from plants or animals. Others are made from nonliving things found in the ground.

Sort them out

Collect the different things you can see in the picture. Put all the things that come from plants and animals into one group. Put those made of nonliving materials in another group.

brick

kitch foil

cotton blouse

pot mu

silk scarf

glass

leather shoe

spoon

paper

stones

wood

woolen glove

plastic bag

Toy tent

We use materials like bricks, wood, and glass to build houses. You can make a tent out of wood and plastic.

3 Tape together pieces of plastic to make a big square. It should be large enough to cover the sticks.

1 Get six small wood sticks. Tie the tops together tightly with string. Put pieces of modeling clay on the other ends of the sticks.

4 Cut a small hole in the center of the plastic. Put it over the top of the sticks. Tape the plastic in place. Cut a flap for the door.

2 Open out the sticks to make a cone shape. Press the modeling clay onto a tray to keep the sticks steady.

Touch and Test

Materials are made of different things. They look and feel different. Some materials are better for some jobs than other materials. We can make up tests to find out more about them.

Feel it

Collect lots of objects as shown in the picture. Gently rub their surfaces to feel if they are rough or smooth. Squeeze them to find out if they are soft or hard. Are they shiny or dull? Make a chart or draw pictures to show what you find.

	hard	soft	smooth	rough	shiny	dull
sponge		√		√		√

Bags of strength

We make tote bags out of paper, plastic, and cotton. Let's find out which material makes the best bag.

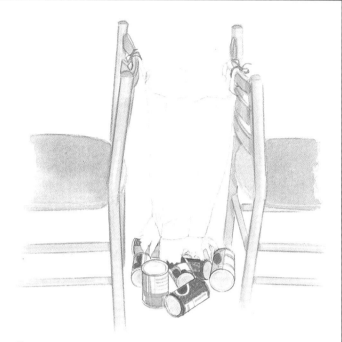

1 Tie the handles of the paper bag to two chairs. The bag should hang between them.

2 Put a can of beans into the bag. Keep adding cans until the bag breaks. Count the cans.

3 Now do the same with the plastic and cotton bags. Can the plastic bag carry more or fewer cans? Which bag can carry the most cans?

The cotton bag should be strongest and carry the most cans. The plastic bag should be stronger than the paper bag.

Stretch It

Some materials stretch when you pull them. When you let them go, they spring back to their normal size and shape. You can have fun with these springy things.

Bend and stretch

Collect lots of objects as shown in the picture. Pull them in turn to see which stretch. Do they spring back into shape? Gently bend them to see which bend. Be careful not to snap them. Make a chart of your results.

Spinning plane

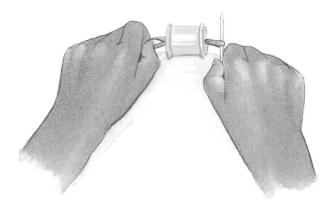

1 Put a thin stick through a rubber band. Push the other end of the rubber band through the hole in a thread spool.

2 Tape the stick in place on the outside of the spool.

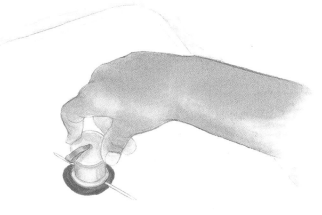

3 Attach this end of the spool to a tray with modeling clay.

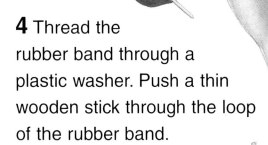

4 Thread the rubber band through a plastic washer. Push a thin wooden stick through the loop of the rubber band.

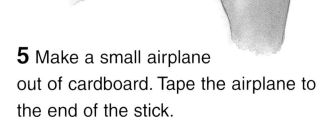

5 Make a small airplane out of cardboard. Tape the airplane to the end of the stick.

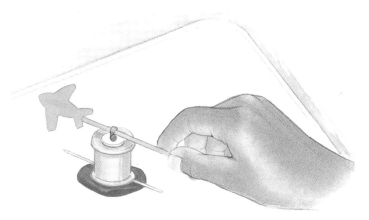

6 Turn the stick several times to wind up the toy. Let the stick go. Watch the airplane spin around.

Metal Mania

Metals are **mined** (dug out of the ground). Most metals are very strong. Some can be **molded** into different shapes.

Look around your home and school. How many metal things can you find? Try to find out what metals they are made from.

▶ Copper can be molded into shapes. It is also good for **conducting** heat and electricity. We can use it to make pots and pans, coins, and water pipes.

▲ Steel is very strong. Knights wore suits made of steel plates to protect their bodies in battle.

▲ Aluminum is light and strong. It is used to make drink cans, aluminum foil, and some airplanes.

Metal mirror

Most mirrors are made of glass. A thin layer of silver or aluminum under the glass makes a shiny layer. You can make an unbreakable mirror from shiny aluminum foil.

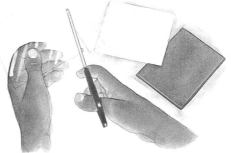

1 Cut a piece of cardboard, aluminum foil, and clear plastic, all 4 in. X 3 in. (10 cm X 8 cm).

2 Put the foil on the cardboard, shiny side up. Put the clear plastic on top.

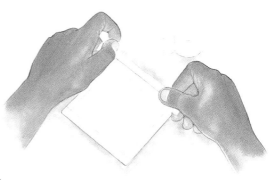

3 Carefully tape around the edges to keep them all together.

Practical Plastics

Plastics are not found in nature. They are made from **oil**. They are strong materials and can be molded into many shapes.

We use plastics to make clothes, bags, and sneakers. How many plastic things can you count here? Can you think of some other plastic things?

Wet or not?

What material would you use to make a rain hat?

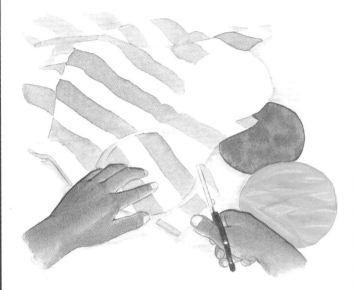

1 Cut out circles of plastic, cotton, wool cloth, and toweling. Make sure they are all the same size.

3 Slowly pour a tablespoon of water onto the center of the material. What happens to the water? Does the water stay on the top, drip through, or soak into the material?

Repeat with the other materials.

4 Make a chart to show what happens to the water.

	stays on top	drips through	soaks in
cotton			
plastic			
wool cloth			
toweling			

2 Stretch the plastic over the mouth of a jar. Pull it tight. Keep it in place with a rubber band.

The plastic does not let any water through. It would make the best rain hat.

Wonderful Wood

Wood comes from trees. We use wood to make furniture and in buildings. Paper is also made from wood.

Look at this picture. How many wooden things can you see here? Can you see some things made of paper? Look around your home. How many things are made of wood?

▲ We cut down trees and saw them into planks. The planks of wood are used to build things.

Soaking up

Paper is made from **wood pulp**. Which paper is best at soaking up water?

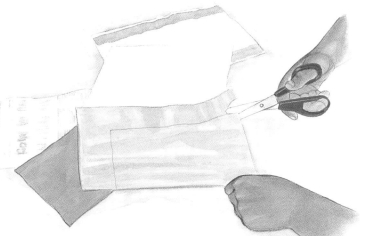

1 Cut pieces of writing paper, paper towel, newspaper, brown paper, and wax paper. Make sure they are all the same size.

2 Feel them. Which one do you think will be best at soaking up water? Which one will be worst?

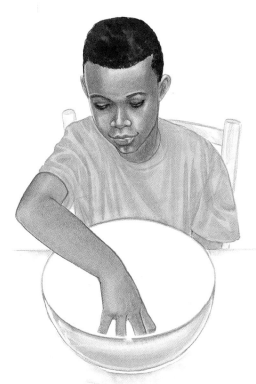

3 Pour a tablespoon of water into a bowl. Soak up the water with the writing paper. Can it soak up all the water?

4 Dry the bowl and repeat with each kind of paper. Which paper is best at soaking up the water? Which paper is worst? Were you right?

The paper towel should be best. The wax paper should be the worst.

Bouncing Balls

Some materials bounce when they are dropped. Other objects do not because they are not bouncy.

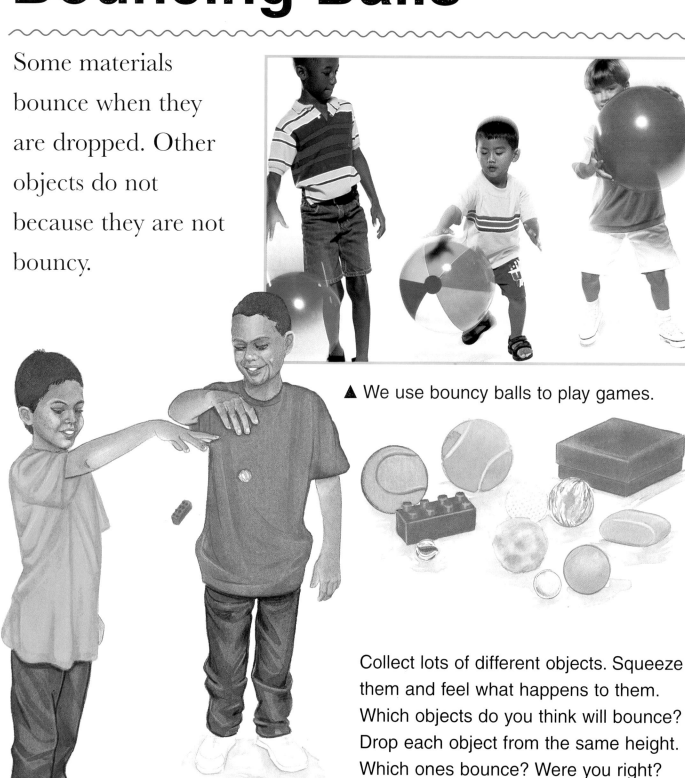

▲ We use bouncy balls to play games.

Collect lots of different objects. Squeeze them and feel what happens to them. Which objects do you think will bounce? Drop each object from the same height. Which ones bounce? Were you right?

Only the rubber ball, tennis ball, sponge ball, golf ball, and eraser will bounce.

Bounce high

Collect a sponge ball, a tennis ball, a wooden ball, and a rubber ball. Which kind of ball will bounce highest?

1 Make a long cardboard ruler marked in inches or centimeters. Tape it to a table leg.

2 Let a sponge ball roll off the edge of the table. Mark on the card how high the ball bounces. Repeat this with each ball.

Which balls bounce the highest? How many times do they bounce? Are the second bounces as high as the first?

The sponge ball, tennis ball, and rubber ball bounce best. They bounce more than once. The second bounce is not as big as the first.

Float or Sink?

Some materials **float** in water. Other more **dense** materials **sink**. We can make some materials float or sink by changing their shape.

Find a floater

Collect several objects as in the picture. Put the things in a bowl of water one at a time. Make lists to show which things float and which sink.

Shape changer

1 Put a ball of modeling clay into a bowl of water. What happens? It sinks.

2 Take out the modeling clay and dry it. Flatten it into a thin sheet. Make it into a boat shape. Put it in the bowl of water. What happens? The clay boat floats.

3 Put a foil food tray in the bowl of water. What happens? The tray floats.

4 Carefully crush the foil tray into a tight ball. Put it into the water. What happens? The foil sinks.

▲ This ship is made of steel. If it were made into a solid ball it would sink. It floats because the metal is spread out over a wide surface.

Water Works

Some materials change when added to water. Some seem to disappear. We say these materials **dissolve** in water. Others remain the same.

▲ Seawater contains dissolved salt. The water **evaporates** in the hot sun. **Crystals** of salt are left behind.

Clear or cloudy?

1 Put a spoonful of sugar in a dry pot. What does the sugar look and feel like? It is shiny, dry, and hard.

2 Pour a tablespoon of water into another pot. Add a spoonful of sugar and stir well. What happens to the sugar? The sugar softens, then disappears. It dissolves.

Repeat the steps with sand, flour, a plastic brick, and some aluminum foil. They do not dissolve.

Magic crystals

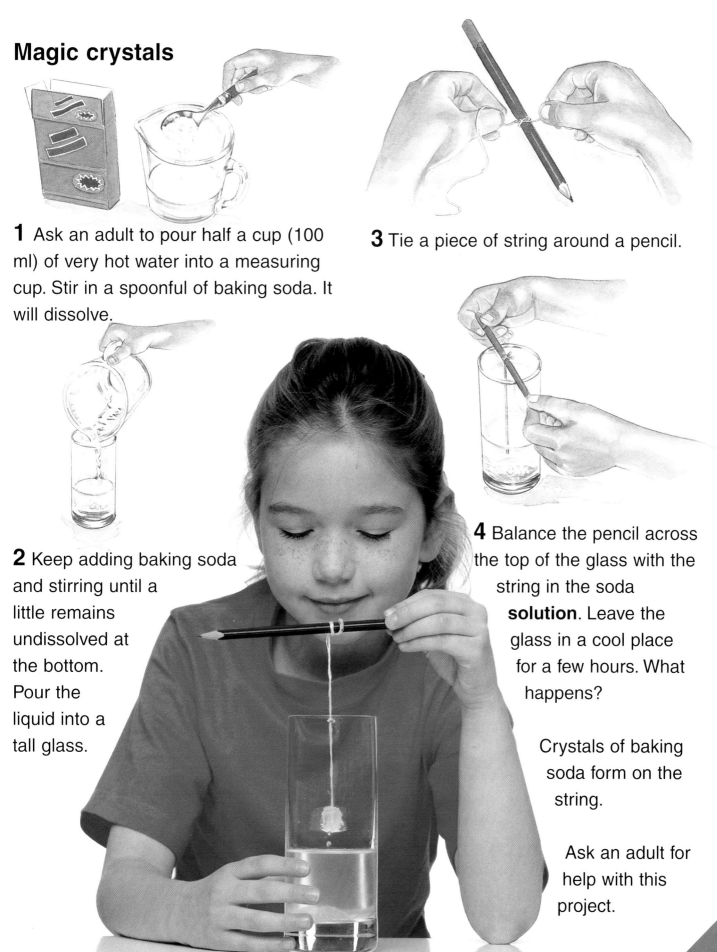

1 Ask an adult to pour half a cup (100 ml) of very hot water into a measuring cup. Stir in a spoonful of baking soda. It will dissolve.

2 Keep adding baking soda and stirring until a little remains undissolved at the bottom. Pour the liquid into a tall glass.

3 Tie a piece of string around a pencil.

4 Balance the pencil across the top of the glass with the string in the soda **solution**. Leave the glass in a cool place for a few hours. What happens?

Crystals of baking soda form on the string.

Ask an adult for help with this project.

Solid or Liquid?

Some materials change when heated or cooled. Many metals and plastics melt when heated. They become **solid** again when they cool.

▶ This volcano is erupting. The rock inside a volcano is so hot that it melts. It bubbles out and flows down the sides of the volcano. The liquid rock cools in the air to form solid rock again.

When water is heated it turns into a gas called **water vapor**. If you cool water vapor it turns back into water.

When water **freezes**, it forms a solid called ice. What happens when you heat ice? It turns back into water.

Chocolate rabbit

We can use melted chocolate to make different shapes.

1 Put some chocolate morsels in a small bowl. Add a small lump of butter.

3 Stir the chocolate and butter until they melt.

2 Ask an adult to pour some hot water into a larger bowl. Stand the small bowl in the bowl of hot water.

4 Spoon the melted chocolate into a rabbit-shaped mold. Put it in the refrigerator. Leave it until the chocolate becomes solid. Take it out of the mold.

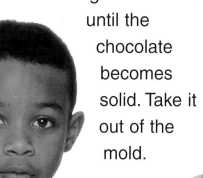

One-way change

Heat can make some materials change for good. They cannot change back to what they were.

▶ When wood burns, it turns into charcoal and ashes. Heat is given off. It cannot change back into wood.

Invisible picture

1 Dip a toothpick into some lemon juice. Draw a picture on a sheet of paper. Let the paper dry. The picture will be very hard to see.

2 Give the paper to a friend. Tell her to put it on a hot radiator. Your drawing will slowly turn brown so she can see it.

The picture appears because the dried lemon juice darkens when it is heated.

Fizzy mix

1 Put one teaspoonful of baking soda into a tall glass.

Be sure to get an adult to help with this project.

2 Over the sink, slowly pour in $1/4$ cup (60 ml) of vinegar. What happens?

The mixture fizzes up to the top of the glass. Baking soda is a **chemical**. The vinegar acts with the baking soda to make a **gas** called carbon dioxide. The fizzy froth is the gas bubbling up in the mixture. You cannot get the baking soda back again.

Materials You Will Need

p. 6 What's What?—woolen glove, cotton material, e.g., blouse, leather shoe, paper, silk scarf, plastic bag, metal teaspoon, brick, pottery mug, drinking glass, aluminum foil, stones, wood, pencil, string, pieces of plastic, six small wooden sticks, tape, modeling clay, round-ended scissors, tray.

p. 8 Touch and Test—stone, smooth shell, marble, bouncy ball, scouring pad, bath sponge, aluminum foil, furry scarf, silk scarf, paper, pencil, string, paper bag, plastic bag, and cotton bag (all the same size), several cans of food of the same size, round-ended scissors. You will need to use two chairs.

p. 10 Stretch It—rubber bands, straw, plastic ruler, modeling clay, copper wire, metal slinky, wooden spoon, plastic brick, hair band, balloon, paper, pencil, tape, modeling clay, cardboard, empty thread spool, two thin wooden sticks, tray, colored pencils, plastic washer or a slice of candle, round-ended scissors.

p.12 Metal Mania—cardboard, aluminum foil, thick clear plastic, ruler, tape, round-ended scissors.

p.14 Practical Plastics—plastic wrap, cotton, fine wool cloth, toweling, jam jar, rubber band, measuring spoons, round-ended scissors, paper, pencil.

p. 16 Wonderful Wood—writing paper, paper towel, newspaper, brown paper, wax paper, measuring spoons, large bowl, round-ended scissors.

p. 18 Bouncing Balls—rubber ball, yarn ball, wooden ball, marble, metal ball, eraser, golf ball, plastic brick, cardboard box, sponge ball, tennis ball, cardboard ruler, pencil.

p. 20 Float or Sink?—bowl, water, stone or metal weight, wooden ball, coin, plastic brick, metal spoon, ball of modeling clay, foil food tray, paper, pencil.

p. 22 Water Works—plastic cups, sugar, flour, sand, small plastic brick, aluminum foil, hot water, measuring cup, spoon, baking soda, tall glass, string, pencil. Ask an adult to help.

p. 24 Solid or Liquid?—cooking chocolate morsels, butter, small bowl, large bowl, hot water, small rabbit-shaped candy mold, wooden spoon. You will need to cool things in the refrigerator.

p. 26 One-way change—lemon juice, paper, toothpick, baking soda, tall drinking glass, vinegar, measuring cup and spoon. You will need a warm radiator to heat the paper.

Hints to helpers

Pages 6 and 7

Discuss the different kinds of materials in the picture. Encourage the children to realize that the woolen glove, cotton blouse, leather shoe, paper, silk scarf, and wood come from animals and plants. The plastic bag, metal teaspoon, brick, pottery mug, drinking glass, aluminum foil, and stones are made of nonliving materials.

Pages 8 and 9

Encourage the child to think of different ways to group the objects. Suggest other ways to test the strength of the materials, e.g., stretching, tearing, and bending.

Pages 10 and 11

Explain that when things stretch, they change shape. Introduce the word *elastic* and let children pull rubber bands to see how far they stretch. Make sure they don't let go of rubber bands near their faces. Find out how far a rubber band can be stretched before it breaks or won't return to its original size. Talk about the uses of elastic things, e.g., trampolines, tires, and springs.

Explain that the wound-up rubber band has been stretched and has stored energy. As the band unwinds, it turns the stick.

Pages 12 and 13

Ask the child to look at and feel different metals. Discuss what metals feel and look like—hard, cool, shiny, dull, smooth—are they all the same? Talk about what metals are used for—cooking pots, radiators, coins, cutlery, ornaments, and jewelry. See if all metals behave the same if you try to pull, bend, or stretch them.

Pages 14 and 15

Discuss what different plastics look and feel like—soft, hard, squishy, shiny, dull—and how they behave when pulled, squeezed, stretched, and bent. Discuss the uses of plastics—to make spoons, plastic wrap, and furniture.

Explain to the children that they have to keep everything the same and change only the material to make a fair test. Ask them to feel the materials and talk about when they would wear clothes made from each material. Ask them which material would be best and which one worst at keeping water from going through. Explain why some materials let the water through. The cotton is not closely woven, so it lets the water pour through. The toweling soaks up the water and lets it drip through. Make sure the wool is pure wool and not acrylic. Water only drips slowly through the wool cloth because it is oily and thus naturally waterproof. Mention that this helps sheep in wet weather.

Pages 16 and 17

Discuss the uses of different woods, e.g., to make furniture, pencils, doors, and ornaments. Discuss how long trees take to grow and why we need to protect trees and forests.

Explain to the children that they have to keep everything the same and change just the material to make a fair test. Ask them to feel the materials and talk about which one will be best at

soaking up water and why. Discuss why the paper towel was best: because the others are shiny, stiff, or oily. Discuss why we need different kinds of paper.

Pages 18 and 19

Ask the children to handle and describe the texture of the balls. Encourage them to realize that the squishiness of a ball can affect the bounce. The hard rubber ball bounces best even though it is not very squishy. The sponge ball is very squishy but does not bounce as well. Solid nonsquishy balls like the wooden ball do not bounce. A bouncy ball bounces again because as it hits the ground it is first squashed and then pushed upward. As the ball springs back into shape, it is pushed up into the air.

Pages 20 and 21

Let the children push their flat hands slowly down into the water and feel the upthrust of the water pushing back. Encourage them to feel the objects before they put them in the water. See if they can guess which objects will sink. Objects that are heavy for their size will sink because the upthrust of the water cannot support them. Those that are light for their size will float.

The clay ball and crushed foil sink because the upthrust of the water cannot support them. The foil tray and flat clay boat have a large surface area and the upthrust of the water can hold them up.

Pages 22 and 23

Discuss substances that we use every day that dissolve or do not dissolve. Explain to the children that substances that do not dissolve do not change in water. Talk about whether you can get the sugar back and link it with the picture of salt production. The sugar is the only material that dissolves. The flour is suspended in the water and makes a milky mixture with a layer of flour at the bottom. The flour will slowly settle at the bottom. The sand, plastic, wood, and foil stay the same in the water.

Children should not be left alone to do the activity on page 23. Great care is needed when using baking soda. The soda dissolves in the water; you will need four or five tablespoonfuls to saturate the solution. When the solution cools, the water cannot hold so much soda. The soda turns back into a solid and a soda crystal forms on the string.

Pages 24 and 25

Discuss with the children how things change when heated. Talk about how water changes its state if it is heated or cooled. Discuss how we use melted metals to make things. Encourage them to understand that the materials change from solid to liquid, but they can change back again to their original form.

Pages 26 and 27

Encourage the children to understand that some materials cannot change back to their original form once they have been heated. Discuss how we use this in cooking, for example look at a raw and a boiled egg.

Discuss how many items that we use have been made from something else and that we cannot get the original item back. For example, flour and eggs are made into cakes, potatoes into french fries, wood into paper, and chemicals into medicines.

Glossary

Chemical Any substance that can change when added to or mixed with another substance.

Conducting Letting electricity or heat pass through. Electricity or heat can pass easily through good conductors such as copper.

Crystals Solids with a certain shape. Salt crystals are shaped like cubes.

Dense An object is dense if it is heavy for its size.

Dissolve When some objects are added to a liquid they dissolve—they break down into tiny bits and mix completely with the liquid so they cannot be seen.

Evaporate To change from a liquid or solid into a vapor or gas. When water is heated, it changes into water vapor, which rises into the air.

Float To stay on the surface of water or another liquid.

Freeze A substance freezes when it changes from liquid to solid in the cold. Water changes into ice when it freezes.

Gas A substance that has no fixed shape. The tiny bits that make up a gas are spaced so far apart that they are not held together. They can move anywhere.

Melt To change from a solid to a liquid. When you warm ice, it melts into water. Some metals melt when you heat them.

Mined Dug out of the ground.

Molded We mold melted solids by pouring them into a special container. As the liquid hardens it takes the shape of the container.

Oil A thick, black liquid found in the ground. It is made from the remains of plants that died millions of years ago. Oil is used to make gasoline and plastics.

Sink To go down into water or another liquid.

Solid A substance that has a definite shape that is not easy to change. The tiny bits that make up a solid are tightly packed together. They are linked so strongly that they cannot move around.

Solution The fluid that results when a solid is dissolved in a liquid.

Water vapor Very tiny droplets of water in the air. They are too small for you to see.

Wood pulp Tiny bits of wood mixed with water to make a paste.

Further reading

Cash, Terry. *101 Physics Tricks: Fun Experiments with Everyday Materials*. New York: Sterling Publications, 1992.

Churchill, E. Richard. *365 Simple Experiments with Everyday Materials*. New York: Black Dog & Leventhal, 1997.

Zweifel, Frances. *Amazing Science Experiments with Everyday Materials*. New York: Sterling Publications, 1997.

Index